TRACTORS
AND TRUCKS

Pull out the sticker sheets and
keep them by you when you
complete each page. There are also
lots of extra stickers to use in
this book or anywhere you want.
Have fun!

make
believe
ideas

Let's hit the **road!**

Find the missing
stickers.

Sticker cars in the transporter.

3

Strong, busy tractors!

Make the tractor your favourite colour!

Find the missing stickers, then circle the tractor that doesn't belong.

Sticker more hay bales.

Fill the trailer with pumpkins.

Draw faces, arms and legs to create fun fruit and vegetables!

5

Colour the **happy trucks!**

Decorate this truck with spots.

Find the
missing stickers.

Add stars to this truck.

What's in the barrels?

7

Sticker the finds!

Colour the amazing medals.

8

Sticker what's in the **truck!**

Draw yourself driving.

What's hiding in the rocks?

9

Trucks **building** a road!

Find the missing stickers.

What's fallen in the cement?

Find these words in the grid below. Words run across, down and diagonally.

digger   rock   cab   pipe

truck   road   mud   dumper

```
w  d  u  m  p  e  r  p  b  i  n  t  r
w  o  t  u  i  r  o  j  i  e  h  f  i
r  o  c  k  i  u  f  p  o  p  n  s  g
a  c  t  c  x  t  g  n  p  y  e  n  i
t  a  o  t  r  u  c  k  i  r  l  g  f
l  b  n  d  r  a  d  i  g  g  e  r  q
o  s  s  h  m  q  l  t  o  w  s  e  o
r  o  a  d  o  i  a  s  a  m  u  d  w
```

Tractors and tools

Colour the shed, then find 3 tractors!

Find the missing stickers to complete the patterns below.

Tractor race!

Sticker the tractors at the start. Now follow the lines to see which tractor gets to the finish.

Start

Sticker the tractors that get lost on the way.

Finish

Trucks and tractors on the move!

Find the missing stickers.

What's in each suitcase?

Copy the truck. Use the grid to help you.

Draw what's in the back of the truck!

Find stickers to fill the farmer's sacks.

Put **5** potatoes in this sack.

Put **7** red apples in this sack.

15

Ring-ring, ring-ring! Send the fire trucks!

Sticker trucks in action!

Find the equipment.

Colour the helmet.

Which one does not belong?

Sticker firemen at work.

Find the missing stickers.

FIRE

Colour the
fire truck.

17

Monster machines!

Design a cool monster truck.

Sticker a number plate.

Find the missing
stickers.

19

Truck repairs

Find the missing trucks.

Help the mechanics order more equipment!

Sticker the items.

1 big hammer

6 bolts

2 oil cans

Find 4 more lost spanners.

Colour the truck so that it looks as good as new.

Green

21

Tractor **maze**

Find the missing stickers, then follow the maze to find the broken-down tractor!

Colour the wheat.

START

FINISH

Can you find 10 differences between the pictures?

Finish the **building site!**

24

Add stickers to complete the scene.

Draw a driver in the cab.

25

Tractors on the farm

Find the missing stickers.

Sticker the things in the hay bales.

Find 5 little mice.

Find the missing stickers.

Colour the tractor.

27

Hardworking trucks and tractors!

Find the missing stickers.

Find 6 things in here.

Find 4 things in here.

Colour the cab,
then find the driver!

What's fallen
into the hole?

29

A busy **tractor** garage

Use stickers and colour to fill the garage shelves.

Help the mechanic count his tractors.

+ 1 = **two**

+ = **six** 6

Sticker the missing tools.

31

Busy transporters

Find the missing stickers.

Colour the tanker truck.

Find 4 lost wheels.

Decorate the **monster** tractor!

Use your stickers too!

Colour the farm!

Add stickers too!

35

Truck and tractor SALE

Sticker trucks and tractors in the correct colour sections!

Red

Yellow

Blue

Green

Make this truck your favourite colour.

Create cool off-road trucks!

Use your stickers too!

39

Complete the busy roads!

Add colour too!

Pages 2-3

Pages 4-5

STOP

Pages 6-7

Pages 8-9

Pages 8-9 continued

Pages 10-11

Pages 12-13

Pages 14-15

Pages 14-15 continued

Pages 16-17

Pages 18-19

MONSTER 1

Pages 20-21

5 new wheels

Yellow

Extra stickers

Pages 20-21 continued

Pages 22-23

Pages 24-25

Pages 26-27

Pages 28-29

Pages 28-29 continued

Pages 30-31

Page 32

Page 33

Pages 34-35

Pages 36-37

Pages 38-39

·BOULDER·

·MUDDY MAX·

Page 40